All Gone!

A play by Julia Donaldson

Illustrated by Ayesha L. Rubio

Characters

Waitress

Old lady

Kiki

Dave

Jason

Simon

3

A café. The customers are lined up at the counter.

Waitress: Yes, what do you want?

Jason: Soup, please.

Waitress: That's one pound. Next!

Dave: Can I have some chips?

Waitress: That's one pound. Next!

Simon: A cake, please.

Waitress: That's one pound. Oh dear, this job is **so** boring. Next, please.

Kiki: A cup of tea, please.

Waitress: That's …

Kiki: One pound?

Waitress: How did you guess?

The customers go to their tables. The old lady enters. No one notices her.

Jason: Silly me! I forgot the spoon for my soup.

He gets up.

Old lady: This soup looks good. I'll drink it out of the bowl.

Jason: (*at the counter*) Can I have a spoon, please?

Waitress: Here you are.

7

Old lady: That soup **was** good. But I'm still hungry.

She gets up.

Jason: Hey! Where's my soup?

Dave: I need some salt for my chips.

He gets up.

Old lady: These chips look good!

Dave: (*at the counter*) Can I have some salt, please?

Waitress: Here you are.

Old lady: Those chips **were** good. But I'm **still** hungry.

She gets up.

Dave: Hey! Where are my chips?

8

Simon: (*getting up*) I need a fork for my cake.

Old lady: This cake looks good!

Simon: (*at the counter*) Can I have a fork please?

Waitress: Here you are.

Old lady: That cake **was** good.
But now I'm thirsty.

She gets up.

Simon: Hey! Where's my cake?

Kiki: (*getting up*) Oh! I forgot
the milk for my tea.

Old lady: Ah! I like black tea.

At the counter

Jason: Where is my soup?

Waitress: Don't ask me.

Dave: Where are my chips?

Waitress: I don't know!

Simon: Where is my cake?

Waitress: Don't ask me. **I don't know!**

Kiki: Can I have some milk?

Waitress: DON'T ASK ME! I DON'T KNOW!

Kiki: What? You must know if you've got some milk.

Waitress: Sorry. Here you are.

Old lady: That tea was **very** good! Now I'll go to the loo.

She gets up.

Kiki: Hey! Where's my tea?

14

At the counter

Jason: Who's been drinking my soup?

Dave: Who's been eating my chips?

Simon: Who's been eating my cake?

Waitress: Oh, be quiet! This isn't 'Goldilocks and the Three Bears'!

Kiki: Who's been drinking my tea?

Waitress: That's it! I'm leaving!

The waitress exits.

Jason: Stop!

Dave: Come back!

Simon: I want my money back!

Kiki: Me too!

Old lady: (*coming back*) What's all the fuss about? I think this is an excellent café!